# LEARNING TOGETHER

## ADVICE AND INSTRUCTIONS ON COMPLETING THESE TESTS

1.  There are 100 questions in each test. Make sure you have not missed a page.

2.  Start at question 1 and work your way to question 100.

3.  If you are unable to complete a question leave it and go to the next one.

4.  Do not think about the question you have just left as this wastes time.

5.  If you change an answer make sure the change is clear.

6.  Make sure you spell correctly.

7.  You may do any rough work on the test paper or on another piece of paper.

8.  Each test should take approximately 50 minutes.

9.  When you have finished each test mark it with an adult.

10. An adult or parent may be able to explain any questions you do not understand.

# TEST 06

SCORE _____

1. Which letter appears once in TUMBLED but twice in RESTAURANT ?  ( T )

2. Which letter appears once in ROMANTIC but not at all in FORMATION ?  ( C )

3. Two times ten is the same as a number multiplied by four. What is the number ?  ( 5 )

4. A banana and 2 apples cost 33p. Two bananas and 2 apples cost 46p.
   How much is an apple ?  ( 10p )


**In each sentence below TWO words must change places to make the sentence sensible. In each sentence underline the TWO words which must change places.**

**An example has been done to help you.      The <u>wood</u> was made of <u>table</u>.**

5.  The television was <u>breakfast</u> on after <u>switched</u>.

6.  A car outside down broke the garage.

7.  Take great care <u>crossing</u> when a busy road.

8.  <u>Not</u> a pen I can <u>without</u> do my homework.

9.  Making a <u>foolish</u> decision is sometimes <u>hasty</u>.


**The table below gives some information about the subtraction of numbers in the top row from numbers in the left hand column. Complete the table.**

|  | — | 2.6 | 4.1 | 4.9 |
|---|---|---|---|---|
| 10. |  |  |  |  |
| 11. 12. | 7.8 | 5.2 | 3.7 | 2.9 |
| 13. 14. | 5.3 | 2.7 | 1.2 | 0.4 |

TEST 06  PAGE 1.

**In each question below write in the brackets a letter which will complete both the word in front of the brackets and the word after the brackets.**

Here is an example.    ROA ( D ) OOR.

15.  WIS ( P ) EAR.    16.  SEVE ( R ) ANGE.    17.  BOT ( H ) EIR.

18.  SPEL ( T ) RACE.    19.  TIC    ( K ) ING.

**In each line below a word from the left-hand group joins one from the right-hand group to make a new word. The left-hand word comes first.**
  **Underline the chosen words.   An example has been done to help you.**

|     | CORN | FARM | TIME |     | OVER | FIELD | YARD |
|-----|------|------|------|-----|------|-------|------|
| 20. | STAR | ONLY | STIR |     | DEN  | PAD   | TING |
| 21. | PACK | SPOKES | TOP |   | MAN  | SIDE  | WHEEL |
| 22. | TIN  | CAP  | BIN  |     | BAG  | GO    | LID  |
| 23. | COT  | MODEL | FOR |    | LED  | RAT   | RING |
| 24. | UNDER | HOUSE | OPEN |  | FIRE | HOLDER | OTHER |

**Four children A, B, C and D sat a test in school.   A scored 5 more marks than B and 8 less than C.   D scored 37, which was 22 less than B scored.**
**How many marks did each child score ?**

25.  A scored ( 64 )    26.  B scored ( 59 )

27.  C scored ( 72 )    28.  D scored ( 37 )

**In each of the following questions one word can be put in front of each of the four given words to form a new word. Write the correct word in the  brackets.**
**An example has been done to help you.**

|     | board | berry | out | bird | ( BLACK ) |
|-----|-------|-------|-----|------|-----------|
| 29. | take  | stand | line | ground | ( under ) |
| 30. | break | come  | cry | burst | ( out ) |
| 31. | table | less  | keeper | piece | ( time ) |
| 32. | ways  | board | wards | light | (_____) |

Four brothers Alan, Bill, Chris and Don each own a car. Alan and Bill have sports cars and the others have hatchbacks. Bill and Don have new cars and the others own second-hand cars. Only the cars owned by Alan and Don have a radio.

33. Who has a new hatchback with a radio ?                    ( _Don_ )

34. Who has a hatchback which is not new and has no radio ?   ( _Chris_ )

35. Who has an old sports car with a radio ?                  ( _Alan_ )

36. Has anyone a second-hand hatchback without a radio ?      ( _Chris_ )

37. Who has a new sports car without a radio ?                ( _Bill_ )

Complete each sequence by writing the correct numbers in the brackets.

| 38. | 3 | 4 | 6 | 10 | ( _18_ ) |
|-----|-----|------|-----|------|-----------|
| 39. | 1.5 | 2.75 | 4 | 5.25 | ( _6.5_ ) |
| 40. | 100 | 64 | 36 | 16 | ( _4_ ) |
| 41. | 8.8 | 7.4 | 6 | 4.6 | ( _3.2_ ) |
| 42. | 520 | 432 | 344 | 256 | ( _168_ ) |
| 43. | (30,45) | (37,43) | (44,41) | (51,39) | ( _58_ , _37_ ) |

Six shoppers E, F, G, H, I, and J queue at a supermarket check-out.
E is four places in front of I.
H is three behind E.
F is nearer the front of the queue than J.
There are two shoppers in front of G and none behind I.
List the shoppers in the queue from first to last.

44. 1st. ( _F_ )        45. 2nd. ( _E_ )        46. 3rd. ( _G_ )

47. 4th. ( _J_ )        48. 5th. ( _H_ )        49. 6th. ( _I_ )

TEST 06 PAGE 3.

# TEST 08

SCORE _____

1. Which letter occurs once in HEADINGS and twice in THOUGHTS ?  ( H )

2. Which letter occurs twice in PHOTOGRAPHIC and once in INHARMONIOUS ?  ( H )

3. Which letter occurs once in HOUSEHOLD, twice in MALADJUSTED
   and thrice in DIVIDENDS ?  ( D )

**In the sentences below 2 words must change places to make the sentences sensible.
Underline the TWO words.
An example has been done.   The <u>wood</u> is made of <u>table</u>.**

4. The <u>difficult</u> asked a <u>teacher</u> question.

5. <u>Thunder</u> sound of the <u>made</u> me jump.

6. A cat <u>dog's</u> into the <u>raced</u> kennel.

7. <u>Book</u> pages are missing from the <u>five</u>.

8. Television is <u>to</u> very boring <u>sometimes</u> watch.

9. It's <u>sleep</u> for bed and time for <u>time</u>.

**In the following, write in the brackets ONE letter to complete both words.
An example is shown to help you.  Example.   ROA  ( D )  OOR**

10.     HU   ( T ) ORE          11.  SIL   ( K ) ILT

12.     HUR  ( L ) ACE          13.  STAR  ( S ) TEM

14.     PART ( V ) ULE          15.  LAS   ( H ) ERD

**The table below gives some information about the addition of numbers in the left hand column to numbers in the top row.
Complete the table.**

16.

17. 18.

19. 20.

| + | 7.5 | 0.4 | 3.5 |
|---|-----|-----|-----|
| 3.8 | 11.3 | 4.2 | 7.3 |
| 5.6 | 13.1 | 6.0 | 9.1 |

**TEST 08  PAGE 1.**

**In the brackets, write the numbers required to complete the statements correctly.**

21.　　　　( _26_ ) + 19　　=　　45.

22.　　　　396 − 7　　=　　( _389_ ).

23.　　　　5 x 45　　=　　5 x ( _39_ ) + ( 5 x 6 ).

24.　　　　12 x ( _62_ )　　=　　6 x 124.

25.　　　　39 x 16　　=　　( _39x1_ ) + ( 39 x 15 ).

**In each of the following words there are 4 successive letters which make a new word.**
**Write the new word in the brackets.**

Example;　**PL<u>ENTI</u>FUL**　( LENT )

26. CUP<u>BOAR</u>D　(_____)　27. FOR<u>EARM</u>　(_____)　28. S<u>HIVE</u>R　(_____)

29. BA<u>DMIN</u>TON　(_____)　30. GA<u>UNTL</u>ET　(_____)　31. ATMOSP<u>HERE</u>　(_____)

32. Y<u>EARN</u>ED　(_____)

**In the sentences below there are 5 words missing. From the lists A to E choose the**
**MOST SUITABLE words to complete the sentences. Choose a word from list A to fill space A,**
**a word from list B to fill space B and so on.　Underline the chosen word in each group.**

The first ( A ) in the book was rather ( B ) but as the story ( C ) things became more exciting.
The hero ( D ) the ( E ) damsel and finally married her.

| 33. A | 34. B | 35. C | 36. D | 37. E |
|---|---|---|---|---|
| pages | excited | went | fought | <u>young</u> |
| sentences | interesting | <u>developed</u> | imprisoned | only |
| <u>chapter</u> | bad | shows | saw | helpless |
| part | <u>boring</u> | continues | <u>rescued</u> | evil |
| story | short | unfolds | met | capture |

**£1.00 is worth 224 Japanese yen.**

38. How many yen would £2.50 be worth ?　　( _560_ )

39. How many yen would £4.25 be worth ?　　( _953_ )

40. In British money what is the value of 392 yen ?　( £ _1.75_ )

41. In British money what is the value of 672 yen ?　( £_3.00_ )

In each line below a word from the left-hand group joins with one from the right-hand group to make a new word. The left-hand word always comes first.
Underline the chosen words.     An example is given.

|     | CORN | <u>FARM</u> | TIME | OVER | FIELD | <u>YARD</u> |
|-----|------|------|------|------|------|------|
| 42. | BY | STAR | <u>MAD</u> | LED | ARE | <u>AM</u> |
| 43. | UP | <u>OFF</u> | OVER | <u>SIDE</u> | DOWN | LONG |
| 44. | <u>RAM</u> | LEFT | CUT | EVEN | <u>PAGE</u> | STOP |
| 45. | SAY | PUT | <u>DIG</u> | OVER | UP | <u>IT</u> |
| 46. | OVAL | <u>HABIT</u> | KNOW | RING | <u>ABLE</u> | LEDGER |

One year February started and ended on the same day.
The 7th of the month was a Wednesday.

47. How many Thursdays were there in the month ?     ( _____5_____ )

48. What was the date of the third Tuesday ?     ( ___20th___ )

49. What day was the 19th of February ?     ( __Monday__ )

50. What date was the last Saturday in January?     ( ___27th___ )

51. What date was the second Tuesday in March ?     ( ___12th___ )

In the questions below give the next number in each series.

| 52. | 3 | 4 | 7 | 12 | ( ___19___ ) |
|-----|---|---|---|----|------|
| 53. | 2 | 6 | 18 | 54 | ( ___162___ ) |
| 54. | 21.5 | 17 | 12.5 | 8 | ( ___3·5___ ) |
| 55. | 8.8 | 8.2 | 7.6 | 7.0 | ( ___6·4___ ) |
| 56. | 4.83 | 5.34 | 5.85 | 6.36 | ( ___6·87___ ) |

TEST 08  PAGE 3.

In the sentences below there are 5 words missing. From the lists A to E choose the MOST SUITABLE words to complete the sentences. Choose a word from list A to fill space A, a word from list B to fill space B and so on.
<u>Underline the chosen word in each group.</u>

Gasping for breath the runner made a ( A ) desperate ( B ) for the tape. ( C ) he collapsed ( D ) on the road, officials covered him with a blanket and then ( E ) him to a nearby hall.

| (50) A | (51) B | (52) C | (53) D | (54) E |
|--------|--------|--------|--------|--------|
| most | chase | Why | weary | sent |
| hopeful | go | Quickly | <u>unconscious</u> | pointed |
| great | <u>spurt</u> | But | tired | directed |
| <u>last</u> | bounce | <u>As</u> | over | ushered |
| big | fling | for | down | <u>carried</u> |

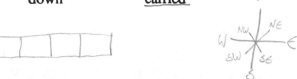

Five towns are situated close together. Town A is North East of town B and South East of town C.  C is North of B and West of town D which is North East of A.  Town E is South of D and East of B.  Which direction is it from ?

55. Town C to town E. (_____)       56. Town D to town B. (_____)

57. Town A to town E. (_____)       58. Town E to town C. (_____)

In the following questions the numbers in the second column are formed from the numbers in the first column by using the same rule.
Put the correct answer in the bracket for each question.

59.  40 ——> 12       60.   1 ——> 1       61.   36 ——> 17

     32 ——> 10             3 ——> 27             28 ——> 13

     24 ——> 8              4 ——> 64             22 ——> 10

      4 ——> ( 6 )          5 ——> (___)          14 ——> (___)

62.  2 ——> 16       63.   1 ——> 12

     5 ——> 49             3 ——> 16

     7 ——> 81             4 ——> 18

     9 ——> (___)          6 ——> ( 20 )

TEST 06  PAGE 4.

**Five girls A, B, C, D and E played with counters.**
**At the beginning A, B and C had 12 counters each and D and E had 15 each.**
**A got 1 from C and 2 from E.    B gave 4 to C and the same to A.**
**D got 1 from everyone else and E got 4 from D and gave two to B.**

64. Who ended with the same number she started with ?            (_____)

65. Who had the least at the end ?            (_____)

66. Who finished with the most ?            (_____)

67. Which two girls had the same number at the end ?            (_____,____)

68. Which two girls had half the total number of counters
      between them at the end ?            (_____)

**There are 6 shops in a block - a shoe shop, bakery, grocer, chemist, hardware and pet shop.**
**The bakery is 3 shops from the pet shop and 1 from the shoe shop.**
**The hardware shop is at one end of the block and 4 shops from the chemist.**
**The shoe shop is closer to the chemist than to the hardware shop.**

**List the shops, starting from the hardware shop.**

| hardware | 69. | 70. | 71. | 72. | 73. |
|---|---|---|---|---|---|
| | | | | | |

**RHOMBUS   TRAPEZIUM   PARALLELOGRAM   RECTANGLE   KITE**
**The above are all quadrilaterals and are defined below.**
**Beside each definition write the name of the shape.**

74.   The four sides are equal in length
      but the angles are not right angles.            (_____)

75.   Made up of 2 pairs of parallel lines.
      The opposite sides are equal and all
      the angles are right angles.            (_____)

76.   There are 2 pairs of equal sides which
      are not opposite to each other.            (_____)

77.   A quadrilateral with one pair of sides
      parallel.            (_____)

78.   Opposite sides and angles equal.
      Two pairs of parallel lines.            (_____)

**The table below shows the number of pupils in a school who attended after-school activities.**

|                   | P4 | P5 | P6 | P7 |
|-------------------|----|----|----|----|
| Folk Dancing.     | 10 | 6  | 5  | 3  |
| Football + Hockey.| 7  | 13 | 15 | 19 |
| Cookery.          | 6  | 8  | 5  | 8  |
| Choir.            | 7  | 5  | 6  | 4  |

79. Which activity becomes more popular as children get older ?    (_____)

80. Which activity becomes less popular as children get older ?    (_____)

81. Which activity is the second most popular ?    (_____)

82. Which activity has exactly half as many taking part as another one has? (_____)

83. It started to rain and all the football and hockey players were divided
    equally among the other clubs. How many were then at folk dancing?    (_____)


**In a number system**

| | | | | | |
|---|---|---|---|---|---|
| 1  | is written as | ~\ | 2 | is written as | ~\ ~\ |
| 3  | is written as | >< | 4 | is written as | >< ~\ |
| 6  | is written as | >< >< | 8 | is written as | >< >< ~\ ~\ |
| 10 | is written as | [] | | | |

**Which numbers are represented by the following ?**

84. >< >< ~\          (_____)          85. [] >< ~\ ~\          (_____)

86. [] >< >< ><          (_____)          87. [] [] >< >< ~\          (_____)

88. [] [] [] >< >< ~\ ~\          (_____)          89. [] [] [] [] [] >< ~\ ~\          (_____)

A bus and a train make the same journey between two towns A and E. They stop at three towns on the way. The train leaves 1 hour 20 minutes after the bus and arrives 25 minutes later than the bus. It takes the bus the same length of time to travel from B to C as the train to travel from D to E. The train arrives at C 35 minutes after it leaves A and an hour after the bus. The bus takes 40 minutes more than the train to go from A to D.

|          | BUS   | TRAIN |
|----------|-------|-------|
| TOWN A   |       | 10.10 |
| TOWN B   | 9.20  | 10.30 |
| TOWN C   |       |       |
| TOWN D   |       |       |
| TOWN E   | 11.15 |       |

90. At what time is the bus at C ?                                                (_____)

91. At what time is the train at D ?                                              (_____)

92. How much longer is the journey by bus from A to E ?                           (_____)

93. When the train leaves A which town is the bus travelling to ?                 (_____)

94. The bus broke down at C one day and the passengers travelled
    the rest of the way by train. How long did their journey from A to E take?    (_____)

95. At what time would the train need to leave A each day in order to arrive
    at E at the same time as the bus?                                             (_____)


Alan, Betty, Chris, Dave and Edward are the 5 children in a family.
The youngest is older than 3 and the oldest is younger than 16. There are no twins in the family.   Two children are older than 11. All the ages, except Dave's, are an even number of years. Alan is older than Chris and their ages together make Betty's age. Edward is the youngest and Betty is the oldest.
Give each child's age below.

96. Alan is   (_____)        97. Betty is   (_____)        98. Chris is   (_____)

99. Dave is   (_____)        100.  Edward is (_____)

# TEST 07

1. Which letter occurs once in UTTERANCE, twice in THROUGHOUT and three times
   in AUGUSTUS ?                                                          (_____)

2. Which letter, that does not occur in the word PRESENTABLE,  occurs twice
   in DIMENSION ?                                                         (_____)

3. What number is three times the half of 8 multiplied by six ?          (_____)

4. What is the difference between seven times nine and eight multiplied by five ?          (_____)

5. I get a total of 20 when I add half of 18 to a quarter of a certain number.
   What is that number ?                                                 (_____)

**When completed, the table below gives the answers when the numbers in the left-hand column
are subtracted from the numbers in the top row.
Complete the table correctly.**

|        | 9.7  | 12.2 |
|--------|------|------|
| 6.  1.9 | 7.8  |      |
| 7. 8.  4.4 |   |      |
| 9. 10. |  3.3 |      |

**In each sentence below two words must change places to make the sentence sensible.
Underline the two words.**

**Example.    The _wood_ is made of _table_.**

11. Many books can be learned from things.

12. Swim only safe waters in.

13. My uncle's brother is my nephew.

14. Our the is at the end of school road.

15. The runner fell lap in the last over.

**In each question below write in the brackets a letter which will complete both the word in
front of the brackets and the word after the brackets.**
   **Here is an example.        ROA ( D ) OOR.**

16.   HAR ( ) ARLY.          17.  CRO ( ) ORD.          18.   POR ( ) ITE.

19.   ARI ( ) YE.            20. GRAS ( ) HASE.          21.   BE ( ) UST.

In each line below a word from the left-hand group joins with one from the right-hand group to make a new word. The left-hand word comes first. Underline the chosen words.
An example has been done to help you.

|  | CORN | __FARM__ | TIME | OVER | FIELD | __YARD__ |
|---|---|---|---|---|---|---|
| 22. | SCAR | DOWN | OAR | TANG | SIDE | LET |
| 23. | OLD | UP | THIN | TEN | KING | DEN |
| 24. | ALL | UPPER | THEM | MOST | SELF | TOGETHER |
| 25. | PASS | IN | LET | TIME | PORT | ON |
| 26. | FAR | BE | FULL | AM | HIDE | WEAR |

**£77.80 was made up using the smallest number of notes and coins shown below.
How many of each were used ?**

27. £10 notes ( _____ )    28. £5 notes ( _____ )    29. £1 coins ( _____ )

30. 50p coins ( _____ )    31. 20p coins ( _____ )    32. 10p coins ( _____ )

**Tom has more money than Jim and Paul, but less than Sid and Bob. Paul has less than Jim. Sid does not have the biggest amount. List the 5 boys in order starting with the one who has the least money.**

( least ) 33. _____ 34. _____ 35. _____ 36. _____ 37. _____ ( most )

**In the following sentences the words in capital letters have been jumbled up.
Re-arrange the letters to form the correct words.**

**Example. VESEN is a number.    ( SEVEN )**

38. Mother is KNOWIRG in the kitchen.    ( _____ )

39. I like tea and toast for SAKRBEAFT.    ( _____ )

40. Cartoons on OLETESIVIN are fun to watch.    ( _____ )

41. The chocolate SIUTBICS melted in the sun.    ( _____ )

42. The BILARRY received many new books.    ( _____ )

43. The boy played the EROCNT in the brass band.    ( _____ )

**In a certain month there were 5 Mondays, and the 18th of the month was a Thursday.**

44. If there were 5 Wednesdays, what was the date of the last day of the month ?   (_____)

45. What day was the 29th of the month ?   (_____)

46. What was the date of the second Friday in the month ?   (_____)

47. How many Tuesdays were there in the month ?   (_____)

48. Which of the months April, June or August could it have been ?   (_____)


**In each line below, the first word can be changed into the last word in three stages. Only one letter can be replaced at a time and proper words must be made each time.**
**An example has been done to help you.**

        tide      ( ride )     ( rode )     rope

49.     dear    (_____)  (_____)   peep

50.     lump    (_____)  (_____)   came

51.     work    (_____)  (_____)   here

52.     wood    (_____)  (_____)   hard


**Five children, Bob, Mike, Stan, Victor and Ken have a school bag each.  Bob and Victor have leather bags and the others have canvas ones.  Only Bob and Ken have bags with zips.**
**Stan and Bob have outside and inside pockets in their bags.   The others have only inside pockets.**

53. Who has a leather bag with a zip ?   (_____)

54. What is the bag with an outside pocket and no zip made of ?   (_____)

55. Who has a canvas bag with a zip and no outside pockets ?   (_____)

56. Who has a canvas bag with no zip but with a full set of pockets ?   (_____)

57. How many children have bags that are not canvas, have no zips and
     have inside pockets ?   (_____)

# TEST 08

1. Which letter occurs once in HEADINGS and twice in THOUGHTS ?    ( H )

2. Which letter occurs twice in PHOTOGRAPHIC and once in INHARMONIOUS ?    ( H )

3. Which letter occurs once in HOUSEHOLD, twice in MALADJUSTED
   and thrice in DIVIDENDS ?    ( D )

In the sentences below 2 words must change places to make the sentences sensible.
Underline the TWO words.
An example has been done.    The <u>wood</u> is made of <u>table</u>.

4. The <u>difficult</u> asked a <u>teacher</u> question.

5. <u>Thunder</u> sound of <u>the</u> made me jump.

6. A <u>cat</u> dog's into the <u>raced</u> kennel.

7. <u>Book</u> pages are missing from the <u>five.</u>

8. Television is <u>to</u> very boring sometimes <u>watch.</u>

9. It's <u>sleep</u> for bed and time for <u>time.</u>

In the following, write in the brackets ONE letter to complete both words.
An example is shown to help you.  Example.    ROA  ( D )  OOR

10.    HU  ( G )  ORE        11.  SIL  ( K )  ILT

12.    HUR  ( )  ACE        13.  STAR  ( S )  TEM

14.    PART  ( Y )  ULE        15.  LAS  ( H )  ERD

The table below gives some information about the addition of numbers in the left hand column to numbers in the top row.
Complete the table.

| 16. | + | 7.5 | | 3.5 |
|---|---|---|---|---|
| 17. 18. | 3.8 | | 4.2 | |
| 19. 20. | 5.6 | | | 9.1 |

TEST 08  PAGE 1.

**In the brackets, write the numbers required to complete the statements correctly.**

21.       (_____) + 19    =    45.

22.         396 − 7    =    (_____).

23.         5 x 45    =    5 x (_____) + ( 5 x 6 ).

24.     12 x (_____)    =    6 x 124.

25.        39 x 16    =    (_____) + ( 39 x 15 ).

**In each of the following words there are 4 successive letters which make a new word.
Write the new word in the brackets.**

**Example;  PL<u>ENT</u>IFUL  ( LENT )**

26. CUPBOARD    (_____)   27. FOREARM    (_____)   28. SHIVER       (_____)

29. BADMINTON   (_____)   30. GAUNTLET   (_____)   31. ATMOSPHERE   (_____)

32. YEARNED      (_____)

**In the sentences below there are 5 words missing. From the lists A to E choose the
MOST SUITABLE words to complete the sentences. Choose a word from list A to fill space A,
a word from list B to fill space B and so on.  Underline the chosen word in each group.**

The first ( A ) in the book was rather ( B ) but as the story ( C ) things became more exciting.
The hero ( D ) the ( E ) damsel and finally married her.

| 33. A | 34. B | 35. C | 36. D | 37. E |
|---|---|---|---|---|
| pages | excited | went | fought | young |
| sentences | interesting | developed | imprisoned | only |
| chapter | bad | shows | saw | helpless |
| part | boring | continues | rescued | evil |
| story | short | unfolds | met | capture |

**£1.00 is worth 224 Japanese yen.**

38. How many yen would £2.50 be worth ?      (_____)

39. How many yen would £4.25 be worth ?      (_____)

40. In British money what is the value of 392 yen ?   (_£_____)

41. In British money what is the value of 672 yen ?   (_£_____)

In each line below a word from the left-hand group joins with one from the right-hand group to make a new word. The left-hand word always comes  first.
Underline the chosen words.     An example is given.

|     | CORN | <u>FARM</u> | TIME | OVER | FIELD | <u>YARD</u> |
|-----|------|------|------|------|-------|------|
| 42. | BY   | STAR | MAD  | LED  | ARE   | AM   |
| 43. | UP   | OFF  | OVER | SIDE | DOWN  | LONG |
| 44. | RAM  | LEFT | CUT  | EVEN | PAGE  | STOP |
| 45. | SAY  | PUT  | DIG  | OVER | UP    | IT   |
| 46. | OVAL | HABIT| KNOW | RING | ABLE  | LEDGER |

**One year February started and ended on the same day.**
**The 7th of the month was a Wednesday.**

47. How many Thursdays were there in the month ?          (_____)

48. What was the date of the third Tuesday ?          (_____)

49. What day was the 19th of February ?          (_____)

50. What date was the last Saturday in January?          (_____)

51. What date was the second Tuesday in March ?          (_____)

**In the questions below give the next number in each series.**

| 52. | 3    | 4    | 7    | 12   | (_____) |
|-----|------|------|------|------|----------|
| 53. | 2    | 6    | 18   | 54   | (_____) |
| 54. | 21.5 | 17   | 12.5 | 8    | (_____) |
| 55. | 8.8  | 8.2  | 7.6  | 7.0  | (_____) |
| 56. | 4.83 | 5.34 | 5.85 | 6.36 | (_____) |

A child emptied her money box and had the following coins; four £1 coins, seven 50p coins twelve 20p coins, nineteen 10p coins, fourteen 5p coins.

57. What was the total amount of money ?                                   (_£_____)

58. How much more would she need to buy a toy at £15.99 ?                  (_£_____)

59. By how much did the value of the 20p coins exceed the value of the 5p coins ?   (_£_____)

60. Would it have been possible to change the coins of lesser value than 50p to
    an exact number of £1 coins ?                                         (_____)

| Number of children | ? | 15 | 8 | 6 | 2 | 1 |
|---|---|---|---|---|---|---|
| Number of pets kept by each child | 0 | 1 | 2 | 3 | 4 | 5 |

The table above shows the results of a survey on the pets kept by 40 children.

61. How many children kept no pets ?                      (_____)

62. How many children with pets kept less than 3 ?        (_____)

63. How many children kept more than 3 pets ?            (_____)

64. What fraction of the children did not keep pets ?     (_____)

Seven boys Alan, Bert, Colin, Don, Ed, Fred and George have a different number of marbles
each. Each boy has more than 1 marble but less than 12 marbles. Colin has an odd number
which is one third of Bert's. Fred has 4 less than a dozen. Ed has twice as many as Don.
Alan and Don together have the same amount as George, who has the most.
How many marbles do they each have ?

65. Alan (_____)    66. Bert (_____)    67. Colin (_____)    68. Don (_____)

69. Ed   (_____)    70. Fred (_____)    71. George (_____)

In each question below a boy ALWAYS STARTS OFF facing NORTH WEST. (NW)

72. In what direction is he facing if he makes a quarter turn anti-clockwise ?   (_____)

73. In what direction is he facing if he makes a three-quarter turn clockwise ?  (_____)

74. In what direction is he facing if he makes a quarter turn anti-clockwise
    and then a half turn clockwise ?                                             (_____)

75. In what direction is he facing if he makes a three-quarter turn and a
    half turn clockwise, and finally a quarter turn anti-clockwise?              (_____)

In each of the following questions one word can be put in front of each of the four given words to form a new word.   Write the correct word in the brackets.

An example has been done to help you.        board   berry   out   bird        ( BLACK )

76.  mill        fall        shield        screen        (_____)

77.  shot        less        thirsty        shed        (_____)

78.  card        man        mark        master        (_____)

79.  age        hole        kind        slaughter        (_____)

80.  scape        mark        lord        slide        (_____)


The table below gives the time in seconds taken by 4 children to swim distances of 1,  2  and  5 lengths of a swimming pool.

| No. of LENGTHS | 1 | 2 | 5 |
|---|---|---|---|
| TOM | 23 | 59 | 218 |
| BETTY | 34 | 85 | 315 |
| SIMON | 28 | 70 | 256 |
| RUTH | 32 | 81 | 289 |

81. Which child swam 5 lengths the quickest ?        (_____)

82. Which child took approximately 10 times as long to swim  5 lengths
    as Simon took to swim 1 length ?        (_____)

83. For which child was the difference in time for swimming 1 length
    and 2 lengths the greatest ?        (_____)

84. For which child was the difference in time for swimming 1 length
    and 5 lengths the least ?        (_____)

Six girls  A, B, C, D, E and  F stand in a straight line.

Neither A nor B is at the end of the line.
No one is further right than C.
E is beside neither C nor A.
D is beside E and B.
F is one of the girls in the middle.

List the girls in order.


LEFT   85. (__)   86. (__)   87. (__)   88. (__)   89. (__)   90. (__)   RIGHT



At a party six chairs are placed in 2 rows opposite one another.
In one row the chairs are numbered 1, 3, 5.
In the opposite row they are numbered 2, 4, 6.
Chair 1 is opposite chair 2.
Chair 3 is opposite 4 and 5 is opposite 6.
Six children A, B, C, D, E and  F sit on the chairs.
F is on an even numbered chair opposite to E but he does not sit on chair number 6.
A is not beside B, and D is not beside E.   A and D sit on centre chairs.

Music is played and the children change seats.
C changes with F.
E changes with D.
B and A change.

91.  Who sits on chair number 4 ?                   (_____)

92.  On which chair does F sit ?                     (_____)

93.  On which chair does D sit ?                     (_____)

94.  Who sits opposite C ?                           (_____)

95.  Who sits on chair number 3 ?                    (_____)

Traffic signals for drivers and pedestrians have two sets of lights.

Set A.   Red, green and amber for drivers.

Set B.   Green man and red man lights for pedestrians.
         Pedestrians cross when the green man shows.

The following settings occur one after the other and then the pattern is repeated.

| | RED | AMBER | GREEN | GREEN MAN | RED MAN |
|---|---|---|---|---|---|
| Drivers Stop. | ON | OFF | OFF | ON | OFF |
| Drivers prepare to Start. | ON | ON | OFF | OFF | ON |
| Drivers Go. | OFF | OFF | ON | OFF | ON |
| Drivers Stop. | OFF | ON | OFF | OFF | ON |

96. A driver approaches red and amber lights.
When these lights change, which man will light up for pedestrians ?      (_____)

97. When the red man is not on, which light for drivers must be on ?      (_____)

98. When the same colour is showing for both drivers and pedestrians,
what other colour is showing ?      (_____)

99. When three of the five lights are on is it safe for pedestrians to cross ?      (_____)


100. If the green man is not showing, which colours for drivers
could be on ?      (_____)

The information below is about 4 boys A, B, C, and D and the hobbies they enjoy.
A and B are the only two who like both reading and football.
B and D are the only two who like both football and painting.
C and A are the only two who like both stamping collecting and cycling.

56. Who likes football but not painting ?        (_____)

57. Who likes cycling but not football ?        (_____)

58. Which hobby does A not have ?        (_____)

59. Which footballer paints and reads ?        (_____)

60. Which cyclist collects stamps but does not read ?        (_____)

61. Which hobby is the most popular?        (_____)

F, G, H, I and J are 5 points on a map. I is 6 km due south of F and 5 km due east of G.
H is due east of F.  J is 7km due east of I and directly south of H.

62. Which point is south-east of F ?        (_____)

63. Which point is north-east of I ?        (_____)

64. Which point is 12 km due west of J ?        (_____)

65. If I travel 7 km east of F and then  6 km south, at which point would I be ?        (_____)

66. If I travel from G to H by going through I and F, how far is the journey ?        (_____km_)

67. If I travel directly from J to G and then through I to F, how far is the journey ?        (_____km_)

In each line below, the first word can be changed into the last word in  three stages. Only one
letter can be replaced at a time and proper words must be made each time.

An example has been done to help you.        tide        ( ride )        ( rode )        rope

68.        time        (          )        (          )        lane

69.        weir        (          )        (          )        team

70.        pack        (          )        (          )        rice

71.        pint        (          )        (          )        lane

72.        work        (          )        (          )        load

In the following questions the numbers in the second column are formed from the numbers in the first column by using the same rule.
Put the correct answer in the bracket for each question.

73.  144 ——> 10          74.  2 ——> 5           75.  5 ——> 26

     81 ——> 7                  6 ——> 15               7 ——> 50

     49 ——> 5                 12 ——> 30               9 ——> 82

     25 ——> (___)            16 ——> (___)           11 ——> (___)


76.  22 ——> 33           77.  1 ——> 1           78.  10 ——> 10

     26 ——> 39                 2 ——> 8               15 ——> 20

     28 ——> 42                 4 ——> 64              18 ——> 26

     40 ——> (___)              6 ——> (___)           22 ——> (___)


£43.75 was made up using the smallest number of notes and coins shown
below.  How many of each were used ?

79. £5 notes (_____)    80. £1 coins (_____)    81. 20p coins (_____)

82. 2p coins (_____)    83. 1p coins (_____)


In each of the following questions one word can be put in front of each of the four given words
to form a new word.  Write the correct word in the brackets.

An example is done to help you.          board   berry   out   bird     ( BLACK )

84.     town      pour      cast      stairs      (_____)

85.     sick      work      land      less        (_____)

86.     burn      day       rise      set         (_____)

87.     coat      over      table     stile       (_____)

88.     ward      roar      set       stairs      (_____)

89.     word      able      age       port        (_____)

**The following questions are about the numbers in the diagram.**

90. Which number is in both the circle and square but
    not in the triangle ?

    (_____)

91. Which numbers are in both the circle and triangle
    but not in the square ?

    (_____)

92. Which numbers appear in all three figures ?

    (_____)

93. Find the sum of all the numbers which appear
    in one figure only.

    (_____)

94. Take the sum of the numbers that are in the square, but not the triangle,
    from the sum of the numbers that are in the circle but not the square.        (_____)

95. Take the sum of the numbers that are in the circle, but not the triangle
    and square, from the sum of the numbers that are in the triangle,
    but not the circle and square.        (_____)

Dot, Amy and Helen each have a blouse, skirt and scarf. Each garment is either black, yellow
or white. No two garments of the same type have the same colour. Each girl wears garments
of 3 different colours.
Dot's scarf is the same colour as Helen's skirt.
Amy's scarf and Dot's skirt are both the same colour as Helen's blouse.
Amy's skirt is yellow and her blouse is not black.

96. What colour is Amy's blouse ?        (_____)

97. What colour is Dot's skirt ?        (_____)

98. What colour is Helen's scarf ?        (_____)

99. Which girl has the black blouse ?        (_____)

100. Which girl has the white scarf ?        (_____)

# TEST 10

SCORE _____

1. Which letter occurs twice in SUPPOSITION, once in SUPPOSE and not at all in SUPPER ?  ( O )

2. Which letter occurs once in BEDROOM and twice in MOMENTARY ?  ( M )

3. Which letters occur twice as often in BELONGINGS as in the word SONGS?  ( G,N )

4. When I subtract 7 from a certain number the answer is 1/5 of 35.
   What is the number ?  ( 14 )

5. Lucy has 3 times as many balloons as Mary and half as many as Pat who has 12 balloons.
   If Lucy gave 2 of her balloons to Mary and Pat gave 1 to Mary,
   how many would Mary then have ?  ( 9 )

L   M   P
18   6   12

**In the sentences below 2 words must change places to make the sentences sensible.**
**Underline the TWO words.**
**An example has been done for you.**      The <u>wood</u> is made of <u>table.</u>

6.   Do not <u>from</u> pages <u>tear</u> the books.

7.   The girls <u>park</u> their bicycles to the <u>rode.</u>

8.   The lights <u>could</u> and we <u>fused</u> not see.

9.   May I <u>door</u> you to the <u>see</u>?

10.   Curly pigs have <u>most</u> <u>tails.</u>

11.   The teacher <u>books</u> the <u>marked</u> in school.

**The table below gives some information about the subtraction of numbers in the top row from numbers in the left hand column.**
**Complete the table.**

| | — | 3.1 | 2.8 |
|---|---|---|---|
| 12. | | | |
| 13. 14. | 11.3 | 8.2 | 8.5 |
| 15. | 4.9 | 1.8 | 2.1 |
| 16. 17. | 6.5 | 3.4 | 3.7 |

In each question write in the brackets one letter which will complete both the word in front of the brackets and the word after the brackets.

Here is an example.    ROA ( D ) OOR.

18.  SIL    (K) ISS          19.  BOR    (E) ARN

20.  MINU  (S) IGN          21.  HEI    (R) EADY

22.  DUS   (T) IRED        ·23.  MEN    (  ) SED

In each line below a word from the left-hand group joins one from the right-hand group to make a new word. The left-hand word comes first.

Underline the chosen words.   An example has been done to help you.

|  | CORN | <u>FARM</u> | TIME | | OVER | FIELD | <u>YARD</u> |
|---|---|---|---|---|---|---|---|
| 24. | CUT | <u>BOW</u> | PIT | | <u>LED</u> | TEN | CHAIR |
| 25. | <u>GO</u> | MAT | CAN | | DYE | <u>AT</u> | SHALL |
| 26. | CUE | <u>ARM</u> | PAD | | ILL | BIT | <u>OUR</u> |
| 27. | COY | CURE | <u>OR</u> | | <u>BIT</u> | TONE | FEW |
| 28. | <u>CAN</u> | ME | DOE | | <u>NINE</u> | ERR | <u>AN</u> |
| 29. | PIE | SEAL | LINE | | PIPE | BALD | THRONE |

In the following questions a letter can be taken from the first word and put into the second word to form TWO new words.   Write both NEW words.

Example.   THEN   TANK     ( TEN ) ( THANK )

The H moves from THEN to TANK  and makes the new words TEN and THANK.

30.  TIRE    HEAD     ( TIE ) ( HEARD )

31.  SWERVE  TIN      ( TWIN ) ( SERVE )

32.  HOST    EVEN     ( HOT ) ( SEVEN )

33.  FRIGHT  HOSE     ( FIGHT ) ( HOSER )

34.  BELOW   FRIGHT   ( BLOW ) ( FREIGHT )

35.  BEAD    POT      ( BAD ) ( POET )

Together 5 children have £8.
The girls together have exactly the same amount as the boys together.
Sue has 50p more than Olive.  Len has 60p more than Fred.
Dave has the same as Len and Fred together.
How much do they each have ?

36. Sue     (£ 2.25     )     37. Olive   (£ 1.75    )     38. Dave   (£ 2.00    )

39. Len     (£ 2.30     )     40. Fred    (£ 1.70    )


A,B,C,D,E,and F are six boats sailing due East in a race.
E is due East of A.   B is due East of E and due West of F.
C is due North of B.   D is due South of E.

41. Which boat is leading in the race ?                    ( F )

42. Which boat is last in the race ?                       ( A )

43. How many boats are further to the East than E ?        ( 3 )

44. Which boat is sailing furthest North ?                 ( C )

45. Which boat is sailing furthest South ?                 ( D )


A digital watch gained time at a steady rate. A man set it to the correct time when he got up in
the morning.  When the lunchtime news started at 13.00 the watch showed 13.10.   Four hours
later it showed 17.18.

46. What time did the watch show when the right time        (_____)
        was 11.00 ?

47. When it was 6 o'clock in the evening what time
        did the watch show ?                                (_____)

48. When the watch showed 16.16 what was the proper time ?  (_____)

49. At what time did the man get up in the morning ?        (_____)


£69.64 was made up using the smallest number of notes and coins shown
below.  How many of each were used ?

50. £10 notes  (_____)     51. £5  notes  (_____)     52. £1 coins  (_____)

53. 20p coins  (_____)     54. 2p coins  (_____)


TEST 10  PAGE 3.

A child emptied her money box and had the following coins; four £1 coins, seven 50p coins twelve 20p coins, nineteen 10p coins, fourteen 5p coins.

57. What was the total amount of money ?                                (_£_____)

58. How much more would she need to buy a toy at £15.99 ?               (_£_____)

59. By how much did the value of the 20p coins exceed the value of the 5p coins ?    (_£_____)

60. Would it have been possible to change the coins of lesser value than 50p to
    an exact number of £1 coins ?                                      (_____)

| Number of children | ? | 15 | 8 | 6 | 2 | 1 |
|---|---|---|---|---|---|---|
| Number of pets kept by each child | 0 | 1 | 2 | 3 | 4 | 5 |

The table above shows the results of a survey on the pets kept by 40 children.

61. How many children kept no pets ?            (_____)

62. How many children with pets kept less than 3 ?    (_____)

63. How many children kept more than 3 pets ?    (_____)

64. What fraction of the children did not keep pets ?    (_____)


Seven boys  Alan, Bert, Colin, Don, Ed, Fred and George have a different number of marbles
each.  Each boy has more than 1 marble but less than 12 marbles.  Colin has an odd number
which is one third of Bert's.  Fred has 4 less than a dozen.  Ed has twice as many as Don.
Alan and Don together have the same amount as George, who has the most.
How many marbles do they each have ?

65. Alan (_____)    66. Bert (_____)    67. Colin (_____)    68. Don (_____)

69. Ed (_____)    70. Fred (_____)    71. George (_____)

In each question below a boy ALWAYS STARTS OFF facing NORTH WEST.  (NW)

72. In what direction is he facing if he makes a quarter turn anti-clockwise ?    (_____)

73. In what direction is he facing if he makes a three-quarter turn clockwise ?  (_____)

74. In what direction is he facing if he makes a quarter turn anti-clockwise
    and then a half turn clockwise ?                                   (_____)

75. In what direction is he facing if he makes a three-quarter turn and a
    half turn clockwise, and finally a quarter turn anti-clockwise?    (_____)

In each of the following questions one word can be put in front of each of the four given words to form a new word.   Write the correct word in the brackets.

An example has been done to help you.      board   berry   out   bird     ( BLACK )

76.  mill        fall        shield      screen      (_____)

77.  shot       less        thirsty     shed        (_____)

78.  card       man        mark        master      (_____)

79.  age        hole        kind        slaughter   (_____)

80.  scape      mark        lord        slide       (_____)

The table below gives the time in seconds taken by 4 children to swim distances of 1, 2 and 5 lengths of a swimming pool.

| No. of LENGTHS | 1 | 2 | 5 |
|---|---|---|---|
| TOM | 23 | 59 | 218 |
| BETTY | 34 | 85 | 315 |
| SIMON | 28 | 70 | 256 |
| RUTH | 32 | 81 | 289 |

81. Which child swam 5 lengths the quickest ?                          (_____)

82. Which child took approximately 10 times as long to swim  5 lengths
    as Simon took to swim 1 length ?                                   (_____)

83. For which child was the difference in time for swimming 1 length
    and 2 lengths the greatest ?                                       (_____)

84. For which child was the difference in time for swimming 1 length
    and 5 lengths the least ?                                          (_____)

Six girls  A, B, C, D, E and  F stand in a straight line.

Neither A nor B is at the end of the line.
No one is further right than C.
E is beside neither C nor A.
D is beside E and B.
F is one of the girls in the middle.

List the girls in order.


LEFT    85. (___)    86. (___)    87. (___)    88. (___)    89. (___)    90. (___)    RIGHT



At a party six chairs are placed in 2 rows opposite one another.
In one row the chairs are numbered 1, 3, 5.
In the opposite row they are numbered 2, 4, 6.
Chair 1 is opposite chair 2.
Chair 3 is opposite 4 and 5 is opposite 6.
Six children A, B, C, D, E and  F sit on the chairs.
F is on an even numbered chair opposite to E but he does not sit on chair number 6.
A is not beside B, and D is not beside E.   A and D sit on centre chairs.

Music is played and the children change seats.
C changes with F.
E changes with D.
B and A change.

91.  Who sits on chair number 4 ?                    (_____)

92.  On which chair does F sit ?                    (_____)

93.  On which chair does D sit ?                    (_____)

94.  Who sits opposite C ?                    (_____)

95.  Who sits on chair number 3 ?                    (_____)

Traffic signals for drivers and pedestrians have two sets of lights.

Set A.  Red, green and amber for drivers.

Set B.  Green man and red man lights for pedestrians.
Pedestrians cross when the green man shows.

The following settings occur one after the other and then the pattern is repeated.

|  | RED | AMBER | GREEN | GREEN MAN | RED MAN |
|---|---|---|---|---|---|
| Drivers Stop. | ON | OFF | OFF | ON | OFF |
| Drivers prepare to Start. | ON | ON | OFF | OFF | ON |
| Drivers Go. | OFF | OFF | ON | OFF | ON |
| Drivers Stop. | OFF | ON | OFF | OFF | ON |

96. A driver approaches red and amber lights.
When these lights change, which man will light up for pedestrians ?          (_____)

97. When the red man is not on, which light for drivers must be on ?          (_____)

98. When the same colour is showing for both drivers and pedestrians,
what other colour is showing ?          (_____)

99. When three of the five lights are on is it safe for pedestrians to cross ?          (_____)

100. If the green man is not showing, which colours for drivers
could be on ?          (_____)

Five children A, B, C, D and E went to school. B arrived punctually.
D arrived after B but before A. C arrived early. E was last to arrive.

55. Who arrived at school at the right time ?        (_____)

56. How many arrived after C ?        (_____)

57. How many were late for school ?        (_____)

58. How many arrived before A ?        (_____)

59. How many arrived before D ?        (_____)


In each of the following questions the word outside the brackets must always have one of the things inside the brackets.
Underline one word only inside the bracket.   An example is shown.

MAN        ( wife, job, car, <u>head</u>, children )


60. HOUSE        ( stairs, garage, roof, garden )

61. CANAL        ( barge, locks, water, holiday-makers )

62. TRAIN        ( passengers, cargo, engine, driver )

63. BOY        ( shoes, limbs, bicycle, sister )


In a certain month there were 5 Thursdays. The 16th of the month was a Wednesday.

64. How many Tuesdays were there in the month ?  (_____)

65. What day was the 1st of the month ?        (_____)

66. What date was the second Friday ?        (_____)

67. Which of these months could it be?        APRIL, JANUARY, JUNE  (underline one)


68. How many Sundays are there in the next month ?

        (_____)

Amy, Beth, Carol, Dot and Edith each have a new dress.
Amy, Beth and Dot have pink dresses, the others have green ones.
Only Carol and Dot have dresses with belts.
Beth and Edith have cotton dresses and the others have linen ones.

69. Who has a pink dress with a belt ?           (_____)

70. Who has a green cotton dress ?               (_____)

71. Whose green dress has no belt ?              (_____)

72. Who has a pink cotton dress without a belt ?  (_____)

73. Whose linen dress has no belt ?              (_____)


In each line below, the first word can be changed into the last word in three stages. Only one letter can be altered at a time and proper words must be made each time.

**An example has been done to help you.**   tide   ( ride )   ( rode )   rope

74.   farm    (_____)    (_____)   wore

75.   lime    (_____)    (_____)   tale

76.   many    (_____)    (_____)   nine

77.   sand    (_____)    (_____)   bunk

78.   hard    (_____)    (_____)   cafe

79.   lose    (_____)    (_____)   fast


Three men and three women sat equally spaced around a circular table. No two men were sitting together. Lisa was opposite Tom. Joan sat opposite Peter with Tom on her right. Also at the table were Sandra and Harry. After a while some of them changed seats. Joan and Harry changed seats and so did Tom and Sandra.


80. Which woman was then beside Peter ?          (_____)

81. Who was then on Harry's left ?               (_____)

82. Who was then opposite Sandra ?              (_____)

83. 84.  Name the 2 men who were then sitting together.   (_____)   (_____)

In the following questions the numbers in the second column are formed from the numbers in the first column by using the same rule.
Put the correct answer in the bracket for each question.

85.  1 ——> 2  86.  2 ——> 13  87.  24 ——> 10

  2 ——> 9  5 ——> 31  36 ——> 14

  3 ——> 28  6 ——> 37  42 ——> 16

  4 ——> (___)  7 ——> (___)  60 ——> (___)


88.  9 ——> 4  89.  1 ——> 4  90.  24 ——> 42

  36 ——> 7  3 ——> 14  36 ——> 63

  64 ——> 9  4 ——> 19  47 ——> 74

  81 ——> (___)  5 ——> (___)  68 ——> (___)


Eight people A, B, C, D, E, F, G and H live in a row of houses.
B is third in the row and C is sixth.
E, H and D live nearer to B than to C.
G, F and A live nearer to C than to B.
D, H, F and G do not live between B and C.
F lives nearer to C than G does.
D lives at one end of the row.

91. Who lives in the first house in the row ?  (_____)

92. Who lives in the last house in the row ?  (_____)

93. Who lives in the second house ?  (_____)

94. Who lives in the fourth house ?  (_____)

95. Who lives in the fifth house ?  (_____)

96. Who lives in the house before the last one ?  (_____)

**The graph below represents the journey made by a motorist one day.**

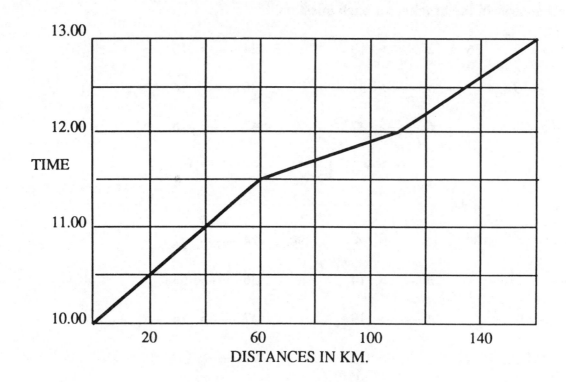

13.00

12.00

TIME

11.00

10.00

20    60    100    140

DISTANCES IN KM.

97. How far had he driven by 11.00 in the morning ?          ( _40km_ )

98. What was his average speed from 10.00 to 11.30 ?          ( _40km_ )

99. How much of the journey did he still have to do at 11.30 ?          ( _90km_ )

100. Part of the journey was along a fast motorway.
     At what time did he leave the motorway ?          ( _11.30km_ )

## Answers to Test 6

1. T
2. C
3. 5
4. 10
5. BREAKFAST   SWITCHED
6. OUTSIDE   BROKE
7. CROSSING   WHEN
8. NOT   WITHOUT
9. FOOLISH   HASTY
10. 4.1
11. 5.2
12. 3.7
13. 2.7
14. 0.4
15. H or P
16. R
17. H
18. T
19. K
20. STAR   TING
21. SPOKES/PACK   MAN
22. BIN   GO
23. MODEL   LED
24. HOUSE   HOLDER
25. 64
26. 59
27. 72
28. 37
29. UNDER
30. OUT
31. TIME
32. SIDE
33. DON
34. CHRIS
35. ALAN
36. YES
37. BILL
38. 18
39. 6.5
40. 4
41. 3.2
42. 168
43. 58, 37
44. F
45. E
46. G
47. J
48. H
49. I
50. LAST

51. SPURT
52. AS
53. UNCONSCIOUS
54. CARRIED
55. SE
56. SW
57. SE
58. NW
59. 3(X + 8) ÷ 4
60. 125 X CUBED
61. 6   (X+2) + 1
62. 121   (X+2) SQ.
63. 22   2X+10
64. D
65. B
66. A
67. C and E
68. A and D
69. GROCER
70. BAKERY
71. SHOE SHOP
72. CHEMIST
73. PET SHOP
74. RHOMBUS
75. RECTANGLE
76. KITE
77. TRAPEZIUM
78. PARALLELOGRAM
79. F. BALL + HOCKEY
80. FOLK DANCING
81. COOKERY
82. COOKERY
83. 42
84. 7
85. 15
86. 19
87. 27
88. 38
89. 55
90. 9.45
91. 11.15
92. 55 MINUTES
93. D
94. 2 HR 50 MIN
95. 9.45
96. 8
97. 14
98. 6
99. 13
100. 4

## Answers to Test 7

1. U
2. I
3. 72
4. 23
5. 44
6. 10.3
7. 5.3
8. 7.8
9. 6.4
10. 5.8
11. BOOKS   THINGS
12. ONLY   IN
13. BROTHER   NEPHEW
14. THE   SCHOOL
15. LAP   OVER
16. E
17. W
18. K
19. D
20. P
21. D or G   LET
22. SCAR   KING
23. THIN   MOST
24. UPPER   PORT
25. PASS   AM
26. BE
27. 7
28. 1
29. 2
30. 1
31. 1
32. 1
33. PAUL
34. JIM
35. TOM
36. SID
37. BOB
38. WORKING
39. BREAKFAST
40. TELEVISION
41. BISCUITS
42. LIBRARY
43. CORNET
44. 31st
45. MONDAY
46. 12th
47. 5
48. AUGUST
49. PEAR   PEER *
50. LAMP   CAMP *

51. WORE   WERE *
52. WORD   WARD *
53. BOB
54. CANVAS
55. KEN
56. STAN
57. 1
58. 5
59. 6
60. 1
61. 4
62. 3
63. 2
64. G9J
65. OT
66. K
67. LFV
68. R
69. NMO
70. 99   X SQUARED - 1
71. 28   (X+1) - 2
72. 21   X + (X-2)
73. 8   SQ ROOT X + 2
74. HONEY
75. WORK
76. HORSE
77. FORE
78. OUT
79. 18
80. 11
81. HOUSE
82. TILES
83. PITCHER
84. THRICE
85. KIJGAF
86. BFCAJGF
87. 6   4   7   2
88. 4   2   7   6
89. 4   2   7   6
90. 7   4   2   6
91. 4   6   7   2
92. 6   4   6   7
93. 5
94. 1
95. 1
96. 8
97. 6
98. 7
99. 2
100. 3

\* There are other possibilities.

\*\* Other combinations may work.

LEARNING · TOGETHER

These are the answers to Book 2 of a set of 4 graded books. A child who has not previously attempted questions of this type may have difficulty with the first few tests. However, research shows that a child's ability to handle and understand these questions generally increases with practice.

## Answers to Test 8

1. H
2. H
3. D
4. D
5. DIFFICULT
6. THUNDER
7. DOG'S
8. BOOK
9. TO
10. SLEEP
11. B, G, M or T
12. K or T
13. L
14. S
15. Y
16. H
17. 0.4
18. 11.3
19. 7.3
20. 13.1
21. 6
22. 26
23. 389
24. 39
25. 62
26. 39
27. BOAR
28. FORE or REAR
29. HIVE
30. MINT
31. AUNT
32. HERE
33. YEAR or EARN
34. CHAPTER
35. BORING
36. DEVELOPED
37. RESCUED
38. HELPLESS
39. 560
40. 952
41. £1.75
42. £3
43. MAD
44. OFF
45. RAM
46. DIG
47. HABIT
48. 5
49. MONDAY
50. 27th

(5. TEACHER  6. THE  7. RACED  8. FIVE  9. SOMETIMES  10. TIME)

51. 12th
52. 19
53. 162
54. 3.5
55. 6.4
56. 6.87
57. £12.50
58. £3.49
59. £1.70
60. YES
61. 8
62. 23
63. 3
64. 1/5
65. 6
66. 9
67. 3
68. 5
69. 10
70. 8
71. 11
72. 8
73. SW
74. SW
75. NW
76. NE
77. WIND
78. BLOOD
79. POST
80. MAN
81. LAND
82. TOM
83. RUTH
84. BETTY
85. TOM
86. D
87. B
88. F
89. A
90. C
91. E
92. 5
93. 1
94. D
95. B
96. RED
97. RED
98. AMBER
99. NO
100. RED AMBER and GREEN

## Answers to Test 9

1. E
2. E
3. E
4. 16
5. 11
6. THE
7. ITS
8. OUT
9. BASKET
10. INTO
11. EAT
12. 1.9
13. 7.7
14. 8.9
15. 5
16. 6
17. 6
18. K
19. 7.3
20. H
21. T
22. R
23. SEA
24. DO
25. HER
26. RAT
27. SO
28. CAP
29. POWER
30. POCKET
31. POETRY
32. POPPET
33. POPPY
34. PUPPY
35. GAVE
36. FOND
37. SHOT
38. DEER
39. FLAT
40. IR
41. D
42. P
43. NRM
44. OMN
45. OEK
46. ROY
47. BOB
48. 11
49. 1997
50. 12 and a half

(6. WHY  7. HORSE  8. WHEN  9. LOT  10. RODE  11. SIT  23. TING  24. NOR  25. RING  26. HER  27. ME  28. SIZE  29. LESS  35. SLING  36. BUOY  37. BREAD  38. STING  39. SHOUT)

51. SEEDS
52. TENDED
53. ESSENTIAL
54. INSUFFICIENT
55. HAMPER
56. A
57. C
58. C
59. B
60. C
61. FOOTBALL
62. J
63. H
64. G
65. J
66. J
67. 23 KM
68. 18 KM
69. 3.7
70. 3.4
71. 1.8
72. 8.5
73. 11.3
74. 2.8
75. 122
76. 60
77. 216
78. 34
79. 8
80. 3
81. 3
82. 7
83. 1
84. DOWN
85. HOME
86. SUN
87. TURN
88. UP
89. PASS
90. 2
91. 5 and 9
92. 4 and 7
93. 52
94. 11
95. 3
96. WHITE
97. BLACK
98. YELLOW
99. HELEN
100. DOT

(19. LINE *  20. TEAR *  21. WEAR *  22. PACE *  70. PANE *  71. PANT *  72. WORD *  73. SQ ROOT X-2  74. 2X + HALF X  75. X SQUARED  76. X + HALF X  77. X CUBED  78. 2X - 10  LORD *  RACE *)

* There are other possible answers.

## Answers to Test 10

1. O
2. M
3. N and G
4. 14
5. 5
6. FROM
7. PARK
8. COULD
9. DOOR
10. CURLY
11. BOOKS
12. 2.8
13. 11.3
14. 8.5
15. 1.8
16. 3.4
17. 3.7
18. K
19. E
20. S
21. R
22. T
23. U
24. BOW
25. GO
26. ARM
27. OR
28. ME
29. PIE
30. TIE
31. SERVE
32. HOT
33. FIGHT
34. BLOW
35. BAD
36. £2.25
37. £1.75
38. £2
39. £1.30
40. 70P
41. F
42. A
43. 3
44. C
45. D
46. 11.06
47. 18.20
48. 16.00
49. 8.00
50. 6

(6. TEAR  7. RODE  8. FUSED  9. SEE  10. MOST  11. MARKED  24. LED  25. AT  26. OUR  27. BIT  28. AN  29. BALD  30. HEARD  31. TWIN  32. SEVEN or EVENS  33. HORSE  34. FREIGHT  35. POET)

51. 1
52. 4
53. 3
54. 2
55. B
56. 4
57. 3
58. 3
59. 2
60. ROOF
61. ENGINE
62. LIMBS
63. 5
64. TUESDAY
65. 11th
66. JANUARY
67. 4
68. DOT
69. EDITH
70. EDITH
71. BETH
72. AMY
73. WARM
74. TIME
75. MANE
76. SANK
77. CARD
78. LOST
79. LISA
80. JOAN
81. LISA
82. LISA
83. +84. PETER and TOM
85. X CUBED + 1
86. 6X + 1
87. (X ÷ 3) + 2
88. SQ ROOT X + 1
89. 5X - 1
90. REVERSE NUMBERS
91. D
92. G
93. H
94. E
95. A
96. F
97. 40
98. 100
99. 40
100. 12.00

(60. WATER  73. WORM *  74. TILE *  75. MINE *  76. BANK *  77. CARE *  78. LAST *  86. 43  87. 22  88. 10  89. 24  90. 86)

* There are other possible answers.